Bubble, Bubble

By Janice Behrens

ISBN: 978-1-338-88858-4

Editor: Liza Charlesworth
Art Director: Tannaz Fassihi; Designer: Tanya Chernyak
Photos ©: 5 Breslavtsev Oleg/Shutterstock.com; 8: stopabox/Shutterstock.com.
All other photos © Getty Images.

1 2 3 4 5 6 7 8 9 10   68   31 30 29 28 27 26 25 24 23
Printed in Jiaxing, China. First printing, January 2023.

SCHOLASTIC INC.

Bubble, bubble, milk bubbles.
Will they pop?

Bubble, bubble, gum bubbles.
Will they pop?

Bubble, bubble, fish bubbles.
Will they pop?

Bubble, bubble, bath bubbles.
Will they pop?

Bubble, bubble, snail bubbles.
Will they pop?

Bubble, bubble, soap bubbles.
Will they pop?

Yes.
POP!